I Love You!

by SCHULZ

CollinsPublishersSanFrancisco
A Division of HarperCollins Publishers

It Was
Love At First
Sight

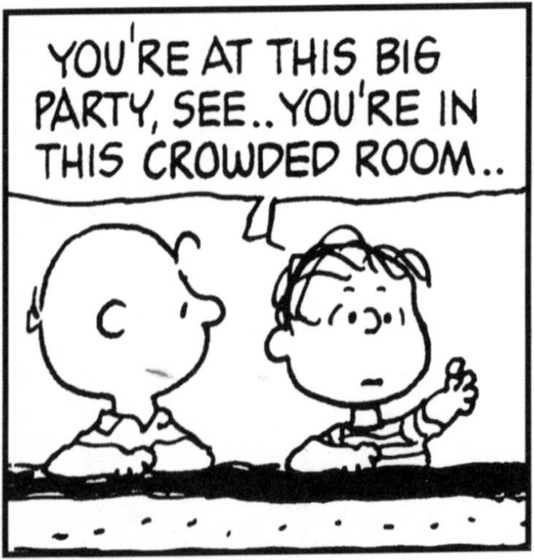
YOU'RE AT THIS BIG PARTY, SEE..YOU'RE IN THIS CROWDED ROOM..

SUDDENLY, ACROSS THAT CROWDED ROOM, YOU SEE THE GIRL OF YOUR DREAMS! SUDDENLY, YOU KNOW YOU'RE IN LOVE!

It
Must Be
Love

I'm
Sleepless Over
You

A Packaged Goods Incorporated Book
First published 1996 by Collins Publishers San Francisco
1160 Battery Street, San Francisco, CA 94111-1213
http://www.harpercollins.com
Conceived and produced by Packaged Goods Incorporated
276 Fifth Avenue, New York, NY 10001
A Quarto Company

Library of Congress Cataloging-in-Publication Number 96-16593
I love you / by Schulz.
ISBN 0-00-225153-1

Printed in Hong Kong

1 3 5 7 9 10 8 6 4 2

A Packaged Goods Incorporated Book
First published 1996 by Collins Publishers San Francisco
1160 Battery Street, San Francisco, CA 94111-1213
http://www.harpercollins.com
Conceived and produced by Packaged Goods Incorporated
276 Fifth Avenue, New York, NY 10001
A Quarto Company

Based on the PEANUTS ® comic strip by Charles M. Schulz
http://www.unitedmedia.com
Library of Congress Cataloging-in-Publication Number 96-16593
I love you / by Schulz.
ISBN 0-00-225153-1

Printed in Hong Kong

1 3 5 7 9 10 8 6 4 2